WHO · WANTS TO · LIVE IN · MY · HOUSE?

Retold by Margaret Beames
Illustrated by Isabel Lowe

Who wants to live in my house?

I do.

Come in, Cat.

And I do.

Come in, Dog.

And me.

You can come in, Goat.

Me, too.

Come in if you can, Sheep.

Can I come in?

If there is room, Rabbit.

What about me?

No, Mouse, there is no room.

No, Mouse, no! Look out!

No room! No house!